Practice in the Basic Skills

English 3

D0552185

Contents

This edition published 2005 for Index Books Limited

Published by Collins Educational
An imprint of HarperCollins*Publishers* Ltd
77-85 Fulham Palace Road
London W6 8JB

www.**Collins**Education.com
On-line support for schools and colleges

© Derek Newton and David Smith 2003
First published 1978
This edition published 2003
Reprinted 10 9 8 7 6 5 4 3 2 1

ISBN 0 00 7727305

The authors assert the moral right to be identified
as the authors of this work.

British Library Cataloguing in Publication Data
A catalogue record for this book is available from
the British Library.

Illustrated by A Rodger

Printed in Thailand

Verbs (1)

A Write down a word which shows how each of the following moves.

1 yourself _____		**6** a horse _____	
2 a dog _____		**7** a rabbit _____	
3 a snake _____		**8** a swallow _____	
4 a cat _____		**9** a salmon _____	
5 a frog _____		**10** a monkey _____	

B Write down a word which shows how each of the following moves.

1 a car _____		**6** water _____	
2 leaves _____		**7** an elephant _____	
3 a ball _____		**8** a kite _____	
4 grass _____		**9** snow _____	
5 an aeroplane _____		**10** a clown _____	

Nouns

A Write out the **nouns** in each of these sentences.

1 The horse was old.
2 I like chocolate.
3 The water is cold.
4 This apple is sour.
5 We ate our dinner.
6 The policeman caught the thief.
7 The cat climbed on the roof.
8 The boys and girls went to the cinema.
9 Leaves fell from the tree.
10 There are many books in the library.

B Write down three things you might see

1 at an airport.   6 at a circus.
2 at a zoo.   7 in a church.
3 in a classroom.   8 on a beach.
4 at a farm.   9 at a railway station.
5 in a hospital.   10 at a garage.

C Write the names of

1 five flowers.   2 five birds.   3 five trees.

1. Church 2. garage
3. farm

Picture comprehension (1)

Write out the story filling in the twelve spaces by choosing your own words.

Sam and Paul _Jamp_ the fence. They couldn't wait to get into the
feled to enjoy the _apples_. They climbed up to a thick _Branch_
and _Scall_ many apples. They also enjoyed _etig_ them! Soon they
saw a _farm_ dog looking up at them and _barking_ The boys were
very _scare_ and daren't _move_. Things became worse, for it was
now _dark_ and the dog was still there. Also, walking towards the tree
was the _Farmer_

eating

Now write what you think happened next.

Punctuation

A Write a sentence about each picture.
Remember **capital letters** and **full stops**.

B Write out these sentences putting in a **full stop** or a **question mark** at the end of each.

1 The Jumbo jet landed safely

2 Have you seen our new caretaker

3 A tortoise has a hard shell

4 We enjoyed Tim's party

5 Will you play football with me

6 Did you see that unusual bird

7 Our lawn needs cutting

8 Why don't you eat your dinner

C Write out these sentences, putting in the missing **commas**.

1 The butcher sells lamb beef pork and sausages.

2 The cricket season is May June July August and September.

3 The sailor had been to China Japan India and Australia.

4 I saw snowdrops crocuses daffodils and tulips in the park.

5 Oak ash beech sycamore and elm are deciduous trees.

6 My favourite football teams are Everton Arsenal Motherwell Newcastle and Linfield.

Adverbs

A Complete each sentence by putting in the right **adverb** from the list below.

  1 Snow fell _____ on the mountain.

  2 The girls ran _____ down the hill.

  3 Anne slept _____ after her long swim.

  4 Our team won the swimming gala _____ this year.

  5 The sun shone _____ all morning.

  6 The old man walked _____ up the stairs.

  7 Bill bought his bicycle _____ at the sale.

  8 The hungry dog ate his food _____.

brightly	greedily	quickly	cheaply
heavily	easily	slowly	soundly

B Add an **adverb** to complete each sentence.

  1 Derek tied the rope _____.

  2 Alan behaved very _____.

  3 Grandma could not cross the road _____.

  4 The nurse treated her patient _____.

  5 When our team scored we all cheered _____.

  6 I can do those sums _____.

  7 Tom painted his picture _____.

  8 The crane lifted the steel bars _____.

Vocabulary and spelling (1)

A The answers to these clues all end in **ey**.

1 Used to open a lock. __ __ __
2 Bees make this sweet food. __ __ __ __ __
3 Like a small horse with big ears. __ __ __ __ __ __ __
4 Bank notes and coins. __ __ __ __ __ __
5 Smoke goes up one. __ __ __ __ __ __ __ __
6 A small animal that lives in hot lands. __ __ __ __ __ __ __

B The answers to these clues all end in **aw**.

1 A metal blade with teeth for cutting. __ __ __
2 An animal's foot with claws. __ __ __
3 Dry stalks of cut corn. __ __ __ __ __
4 Everyone must obey the __ __ __.
5 The lower part of your face. __ __ __ __
6 To make a picture of something. __ __ __ __

C The answers to these clues all end in **le**.

1 A two-wheeled vehicle. __ __ __ __ __ __ __
2 A fruit. __ __ __ __ __
3 A bird of prey. __ __ __ __ __ __
4 A gun with a long barrel. __ __ __ __ __ __
5 Burned to give light. __ __ __ __ __ __
6 A referee uses one. __ __ __ __ __ __ __

Adjectives (1)

A Write out the **adjectives** in these sentences.

1 Jayne wore a pink frock at her party.
2 Our football team wear blue shirts.
3 A big lorry skidded in the snow.
4 Mark played with his electric train.
5 The rabbit hid in the long grass.
6 A tall policeman helped the old lady to cross the road.
7 The tall cupboard was full of old books.
8 "Don't walk on the wet floor!" shouted the grumpy caretaker.
9 The long, thin rope was tied round the fat man's legs.
10 The huge tanker was rolling in the rough sea.

B Fit each of the **adjectives** in column A with the **nouns** in column B.

	A	B
1	juicy	sweater
2	hot	flower
3	fast	hill
4	heavy	orange
5	red	lake
6	loud	dinner
7	woollen	clown
8	deep	load
9	funny	noise
10	steep	car

Pictures and sentences

Write a sentence about each picture.
There are some words to help you.

1 dad   —   spade   —   garden
2 girl   —   bicycle   —   kerb
3 dog   —   cat   —   garden
4 farmer   —   pigs   —   sty
5 mum   —   baby   —   pram   —   pond
6 boy   —   fence   —   trousers   —   nail
7 lighthouse   —   rocks   —   rough   —   ship
8 boy   —   bounce   —   pavement   —   car

Alphabetical order (1)

a　b　c　d　e　f　g　h　i　j　k　l　m

n　o　p　q　r　s　t　u　v　w　x　y　z

A Write each list of words in **alphabetical order**.

1	bark	bench	bold	big	bull
2	acorn	air	above	animal	arrow
3	cut	chess	camel	crow	clock
4	place	puzzle	paint	pram	pencil
5	skin	shed	seven	sail	seal
6	duck	door	desk	dart	dig
7	milk	music	meat	money	make
8	tent	thief	talk	tomato	tie
9	wheat	wasp	wrist	week	wife
10	rhyme	rust	real	rain	ribbon

B Write the word which is **out of order** in each of these lists of words.

1	lamb	leaf	lion	lunch	log
2	nail	nine	netball	note	nurse
3	fall	fell	fill	fox	floor
4	earth	echo	eel	eight	edge
5	germ	ghost	giant	gold	glue
6	help	hymn	hide	hole	hutch
7	jungle	jam	jeans	jigsaw	joke
8	vest	village	valley	volcano	vulture
9	paint	pearl	pillar	present	past
10	dentist	dwarf	diamond	dollar	drill

Joining sentences (1)

A Use **who** or **which** to join these sentences.
Remember: **who** for **persons**
which for **things**.

1 Here is the girl. She is a good swimmer.
2 I caught the dog. It bit the boy.
3 The teacher praised Tom. He had written an exciting story.
4 I thanked the policeman. He found my bike.
5 We travelled on the train. It went to Cardiff.
6 Jim caught a fish. It was swimming in the pond.
7 This is my aunty. She lives in Belfast.
8 Mrs. Rigby has two sons. They are very tall.

B Choose **so** or **but** or **because** to join each pair of sentences.

1 Tim slipped and fell. He did not hurt himself.
2 She had measles. She could not go to school.
3 Brenda returned the shoes to the shop. They were too small.
4 The hotel was burned down. No lives were lost.
5 She could not speak. She had a sore throat.
6 The garage was closed. We could not buy any petrol.
7 We went to the forest. We wanted to see a woodpecker.
8 The policeman chased the dog. He did not catch it.

Gender

A Write the missing words.

	male	female			male	female
1	prince	_____		6	bridegroom	_____
2	man	_____		7	father	_____
3	boy	_____		8	wizard	_____
4	uncle	_____		9	grandfather	_____
5	son	_____		10	god	_____

B Write the missing words.

	male	female			male	female
1	_____	actress		6	_____	waitress
2	_____	mayoress		7	_____	widow
3	_____	queen		8	_____	she
4	_____	niece		9	_____	heroine
5	_____	sister		10	_____	wife

C Write the missing words.

	male	female			male	female
1	_____	lioness		6	_____	cow
2	gander	_____		7	fox	_____
3	_____	doe		8	_____	ewe
4	stallion	_____		9	cock	_____
5	_____	tigress		10	_____	hind

Verbs (2)

A Find the **verbs** in these sentences.

1 The boy kicked the ball.
2 Janet ran down the street.
3 Tim jumped over the fence.
4 The car skidded on the ice.
5 The baby crawled on the rug.
6 Paul ate his tea and then played cricket.
7 The farmer cut the hedges and fed the cows.
8 The queen waved when we cheered her.
9 Sam cut his leg when he fell off the wall.
10 Our cat purrs when I stroke him.

B Write down **two** actions which each of these persons might do.

1 your teacher
2 a policeman
3 a nurse
4 a soldier
5 a cricketer
6 a farmer
7 a joiner
8 your mum
9 a footballer
10 your caretaker

Adjectives (2)

A Complete the following sentences by using the most suitable **adjective** from the list.

1 The _____ lights of the car dazzled me.
2 The _____ girl fell over the stool.
3 It took Jayne a long time to do the _____ sums.
4 The _____ kitten chased the ball of wool.
5 A _____ cloud usually brings rain.
6 The car skidded on an _____ patch on the road.
7 Our chimney blew down in the _____ weather.
8 Jack was an _____ boy and did not do his homework.

difficult	windy	bright	idle
dark	clumsy	icy	playful

B Rewrite the following groups of words, choosing an **opposite** to the **adjective** in each group.
e.g. a **bright** light → a **dull** light

1 a short day →
2 a sad girl →
3 a slow train →
4 a dry towel →
5 a young horse →
6 a stale loaf →
7 a weak lion →
8 a sour apple →
9 a shallow pond →
10 a tame animal →
11 a wrong answer →
12 a polite girl →

Plurals

Write the correct **plurals** of these words.

A 1 dog
  2 box
  3 brush
  4 girl
  5 hand

  6 glass
  7 match
  8 lake
  9 fox
  10 flower

B 1 holiday
  2 city
  3 army
  4 boy
  5 key

  6 story
  7 monkey
  8 pony
  9 lady
  10 valley

C 1 half
  2 cargo
  3 loaf
  4 thief
  5 potato

  6 wolf
  7 volcano
  8 leaf
  9 elf
  10 tomato

D 1 day
  2 scarf
  3 chief
  4 lily
  5 child

  6 church
  7 piano
  8 woman
  9 foot
  10 paper

Pronouns

Remember: a **pronoun** is a word used in place of a **noun**.

A Write out the **pronouns** in these sentences.

1 I am now nine years old.
2 He jumped over the fence.
3 She baked a large cake.
4 Please pass me a ruler.
5 They are going to the cinema.
6 You must eat all your dinner.
7 We enjoyed the party. Did you?
8 There is a dog called Kim. It is an Alsatian.

B Write out these sentences and put a **pronoun** in place of the **noun** or **nouns** in bold type.

1 **Janet** won the first race.
2 The **dog** ran off when I opened the door.
3 **Pat** and **Sue** are busy painting.
4 The **rain** is still pouring down.
5 Peter chose the **flowers** for his mother.
6 **Mr. Clark** dug his garden.
7 Brian gave stamps to **Mrs. Kay**.
8 Tom asked **Bill** for some sweets.

| it | he | they | she | him | her | them |

Adjectives (3)

A Use the vowels **a e i o u** to complete these **adjectives**.

very unkind	c r __ __ l
angry, wild	f __ __ r c __
kind, showing friendship	f r __ __ n d l y
not costing much money	c h __ __ p
not making any sound	s __ l __ n t

B In each line write out the **adjective** which **best** describes the word in heavy type.

1 **elephant**	hungry	huge	tiny	quick
2 **tree**	square	purple	iron	leafy
3 **fire**	blazing	happy	damp	wet
4 **chair**	three-legged	playful	comfortable	sleepy
5 **horse**	smiling	bold	grassy	fast
6 **water**	wet	fresh	loud	woollen
7 **street**	busy	grassy	broken	speedy
8 **gale**	calm	small	howling	warm
9 **orange**	oblong	juicy	green	musical
10 **book**	babbling	lazy	wooden	exciting

C Complete each sentence by choosing a suitable **adjective**.

1 We were very happy when we heard the _____ news.
2 The fireman received a medal for his _____ act.
3 The old lady stumbled along carrying a _____ bag.
4 The boat overturned in the _____ sea.
5 Jean enjoyed eating the _____ pear.

Picture comprehension (2)

Look carefully at the four pictures. Write two sentences about each picture so that you tell the story. Give your story a title.
These words will help you.

man	dig	garden	kettle	bird	eggs
cat	fence	pounce	table	hatched	pleased

Vocabulary and spelling (2)

A The answers to these clues all have **tt** in them.

1 Opposite of top.   _ _ t t _ _
2 Bad.   _ _ t t _ _
3 A small room in the roof.   _ t t _ _
4 A food made from milk   _ _ t t _ _
5 A small country house.   _ _ t t _ _ _
6 Nice to look at.   _ _ _ t t _

B The answers to these clues all have **rr** in them.

1 A looking glass.   _ _ r r _ _
2 Not wide.   _ _ r r _ _
3 The day after today.   _ _ _ _ r r _ _
4 To go quickly.   _ _ r r _
5 A soft, juicy, red fruit.   _ _ _ _ _ _ _ r r _
6 Used with a bow for shooting. _ r r _ _

C The answers to these clues all have **ll** in them.

1 Dancing to music on a stage.   _ _ l l _ _
2 A small bird with a forked tail. _ _ _ l l _ _
3 The colour of buttercup flowers. _ _ l l _ _
4 High.   _ _ l l
5 A dog wears one round its neck.   _ _ l l _ _
6 A number of houses in the country. _ _ l l _ _ _

Contractions

A Join each pair of words together and write the short form.
Remember: the **apostrophe (')** goes where the **i** was.

1 he is   5 that is

2 she is   6 where is

3 it is   7 what is

4 who is   8 there is

B Join each pair of words together and write the short form.
Remember: the **apostrophe (')** goes where the **wi** was.

1 we will   4 she will

2 he will   5 I will

3 you will   6 they will

C Join each pair of words together and write the short form.

1 we are   4 we have

2 I am   5 they have

3 they are   6 I have

D Write these short forms in full.

1 doesn't   6 I'm

2 weren't   7 that's

3 haven't   8 they'll

4 we'll   9 when's

5 they're   10 can't

Groups

A Choose a group name from the list below to complete each line.

1 bear   kangaroo   tiger   monkey   →
2 blue   red   green   yellow   →
3 spanner   saw   plane   hammer   →
4 lemon   peach   strawberry   orange   →
5 van   car   lorry   taxi   →
6 June   October   May   December   →
7 sycamore   willow   beech   oak   →
8 shark   cod   plaice   sardine   →
9 daffodil   pansy   daisy   snowdrop   →
10 robin   sparrow   thrush   duck   →

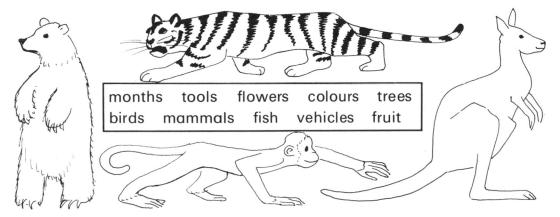

months   tools   flowers   colours   trees
birds   mammals   fish   vehicles   fruit

B In each of the following lines one word **does not** belong to the same group as the others.
Write the odd word.

1 oak   ash   tulip   beech   sycamore
2 England   Jamaica   Canada   Asia   Egypt
3 peach   strawberry   apple   carrot   lemon
4 tulip   daffodil   buttercup   pansy   grass
5 lorry   ship   car   van   bus
6 carpet   stool   chair   bench   settee
7 horse   hen   donkey   cow   sheep
8 knee   ankle   elbow   wrist   face

Verbs (3)

Write out the following sentences by choosing the most suitable **verb** from the brackets.

1 Tim was (hurled/thrown) off his bike when it hit the kerb.

2 Susan (walked/limped) off the field after she twisted her ankle.

3 Peter (stepped/leaped) on to the path as the lorry skidded towards him.

4 When the thunderstorm started we (went/dashed) for shelter.

5 The dinghy's sail was (ripped/pulled) to shreds by the raging gale.

6 The express train (travelled/thundered) through the station.

7 The soldiers (walked/marched) smartly to the palace.

8 The racing cars (drove/roared) along the straight at 260 km/h.

9 The scared pony (lashed/kicked) out at the snapping dog.

10 The water (gushed/dripped) from the burst pipe.

11 The brave man (went/dived) into the sea to rescue the little girl.

12 The thief (snatched/took) the old lady's handbag.

Picture comprehension (3)

Look carefully at the four pictures. Write a few sentences about each picture so that you tell a story. Give your story a title.
These words will help you.

Mark	Darren	zoo	entrance	price	monkey
grab	hat	swinging	bars	elephant	keeper
loaves	trunk	sea lion	leaping	feeding	throwing

Vocabulary (1)

A Which person would you link with each pair of words?

1 hills, sheep
2 tools, machines
3 telescope, sea
4 medicines, tablets
5 statues, stone

6 patient, hospital
7 eyes, spectacles
8 tools, timber
9 chimneys, spires
10 brushes, polish

chemist	caretaker	optician	joiner	mechanic
sculptor	shepherd	steeplejack	coastguard	nurse

B What name do you give to _____?
The first letter of each is given.

1 A woman who serves in a restaurant is a w_____.
2 Someone who draws and paints is an a_____.
3 The place where bread is made is a b_____.
4 Someone who looks after your teeth is a d_____.
5 The place where beer is made is a b_____.
6 Someone who searches for new lands is an e_____.
7 A person who repairs leaking water pipes is a p_____.
8 The place where many apple trees grow is an o_____.
9 Someone who rides horses in races is a j_____.
10 A land where very little grows is a d_____.

Questions

A Use the words from the list to complete the questions.
Don't forget the **question mark (?)** at the end of each question.

1 __ did you put the hamster's food
2 __ is your mother feeling after her operation
3 __ you enjoy your trip to the zoo
4 __ you lend me your bike, please
5 __ of these puppies would you like
6 __ were you not at school this morning
7 __ football boots are these
8 __ would you like to do tomorrow
9 __ you seen the exhibition of models
10 __ said that our team won

will	why	who	have	whose
did	where	which	what	how

B Here are Malcolm's answers to some questions.
Write down a question to fit each answer.

1 I live in Sutton, Surrey.
2 My favourite dog is a Dalmatian.
3 No, my sister isn't married.
4 My dad is a joiner.
5 I live on the fifth floor of Tower Flats.
6 Spurs is my favourite soccer team.
7 Yes, we went to Holland last year.
8 I hope to be an electrician.
9 My mum works in an office.
10 I enjoy soccer, reading and watching TV.

Similar meanings

A For each word in heavy type write a word which has a **similar** meaning. Choose from the list.

1 Paul found the maths **difficult**.
2 Dad took the **cash** to the bank.
3 Jayne was **weeping** because her dog was lost.
4 The joiner will **repair** the broken fence.
5 The **wealthy** singer drives a Rolls Royce.
6 Do you want me to **assist** you to push your car?
7 Carol was glad that her answers were **correct**.
8 Our school concert **commences** at 7.30 p.m.
9 Harvest mice are **small** animals.
10 The plumber is here to **connect** the water pipes.

rich	little	mend	right	hard
join	money	help	starts	crying

B Write out the word in each line which has a **similar** meaning to the word in heavy type.

1 **answer**   shout   reply   whisper   talk
2 **plucky**   strong   shy   brave   lucky
3 **bright**   show   flat   dull   shining
4 **fall**   drop   raise   run   swim
5 **reveal**   have   hide   show   receive
6 **collect** sweep   gather   clean   jump
7 **short**   dark   tall   brief   long
8 **hide**   seek   ask   show   conceal
9 **sketch**   act   reveal   draw   dance
10 **top**   summit   base   middle   bottom

Adjectives (4)

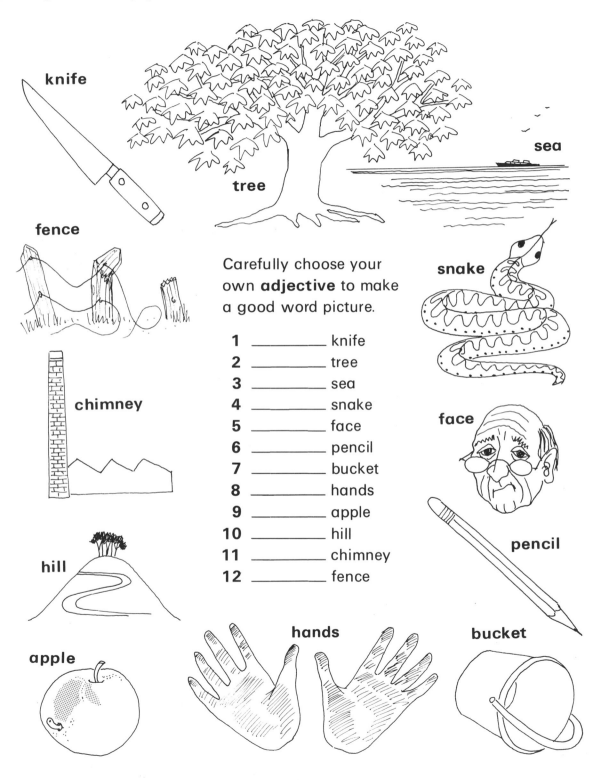

knife

tree

sea

fence

snake

chimney

face

pencil

hill

apple

hands

bucket

Carefully choose your own **adjective** to make a good word picture.

1 _____ knife
2 _____ tree
3 _____ sea
4 _____ snake
5 _____ face
6 _____ pencil
7 _____ bucket
8 _____ hands
9 _____ apple
10 _____ hill
11 _____ chimney
12 _____ fence

Alphabetical order (2)

a   b   c   d   e   f   g   h   i   j   k   l   m

n   o   p   q   r   s   t   u   v   w   x   y   z

A Write the following words in **alphabetical order**.

1	male	marble	mayor	magic	mast
2	paw	pale	page	parcel	path
3	tap	taxi	tale	table	tadpole
4	walrus	watch	wax	wagon	war
5	bend	berry	bell	beach	bee
6	cage	card	cactus	camel	cabbage
7	date	daffodil	dagger	dawn	dark
8	father	fair	farm	face	fall
9	grab	grow	grease	grunt	grip
10	verb	vehicle	veal	vestry	velvet

B Write the word which is **out of order** in each of these lines.

1	bible	bicycle	big	bird	bill
2	cigar	cider	cinema	circle	city
3	deaf	deck	dentist	deep	desert
4	weak	web	weed	well	weigh
5	rifle	rice	ring	ripe	river
6	maid	make	mammal	magic	mast
7	hair	hall	hang	hand	hard
8	fear	feet	fed	ferry	fever
9	nail	napkin	naval	nasty	nation
10	shaft	ship	short	shut	shed

Mixed bag (1)

A Choose the correct word from the list to complete each sentence.

1 The football belongs to him. The football is _____.
2 The horses belong to them. The horses are _____.
3 The book belongs to you. The book is _____.
4 The apples belong to us. The apples are _____.
5 The bicycle belongs to me. The bicycle is _____.
6 The cat belongs to her. The cat is _____.
7 I bought a ball. The ball is _____.
8 Jayne has a new dress. The dress is _____.
9 They have some sweets. The sweets are _____.
10 You have a dog. The dog is _____.

| mine | yours | his | ours | hers | theirs |

B Complete these sentences by choosing suitable words from the list.

1 His face was as white as _____.
2 The miner's hands were as hard as _____.
3 Paul's hands were as black as _____.
4 Helen was as busy as a _____.
5 The stray dog was as thin as a _____.
6 Joan's hands were as cold as _____.
7 The bird's feathers were as green as _____.
8 This parcel is as heavy as _____.
9 My parcel is as light as a _____.
10 Her apple is as sweet as _____.

| rake | honey | snow | bee | ice |
| nails | feather | coal | lead | grass |

Opposites

A Write out the word with an **opposite** meaning to the word in capital letters in each line.

1 UNHAPPY	miserable	sad	glad	ill
2 GIVE	present	own	take	have
3 BEGIN	commence	run	end	start
4 GOOD	nice	neat	happy	bad
5 LARGE	small	thin	huge	tall
6 NOISE	shout	row	quiet	scream
7 CLEAN	bathed	dirty	washed	ill
8 HOT	cold	warm	sun	fire
9 DAY	afternoon	dawn	morning	night
10 SHALLOW	small	thin	deep	paddle

B Write out these pairs of words.
   If they are **similar** in meaning write an S after them.
   If they are **opposite**, write an O.

1 shout   whisper

2 stay   remain

3 found   lost

4 first   last

5 close   near

6 ascend   descend

7 separate   unite

8 careful   cautious

9 front   back

10 clean   pure

11 clean   dirty

12 rich   poor

13 fear   terror

14 bleak   dreary

15 hold   release

16 colossal   gigantic

Comprehension (1)

Littlenose the bee keeper

During the Ice Age, boys like Littlenose ate many of the same foods as we do today. They had meat and fish as well as fruit and vegetables, but they also ate things we would never dream of eating. Caterpillars for instance. Littlenose knew nothing about sugar. He never had sweets to eat, or jam, or sticky buns, or anything made from sugar. Instead he ate honey. Honey was found by taking it from the nests of wild bees. Collecting honey was as dangerous as hunting rhinoceros or elk. The bees may have been small, but they were as ferocious in their own small way as sabre-toothed tigers.

From *Littlenose to the Rescue* by John Grant
Reprinted by permission of BBC Publications

1 How do you know that Littlenose lived a long time ago?
2 Write down four foods he ate which we eat today.
3 What did he eat which you would not like to eat?
4 Write down the three things mentioned in the passage which we eat but Littlenose didn't eat.
5 Name two wild animals mentioned which we can still see today.
6 Name one wild animal from the passage which is extinct.
7 What was used instead of sugar?
8 From where did Littlenose get his honey?
9 Why was collecting honey dangerous?
10 How do you think the bees defended their nests?

Abbreviations

A Write the **abbreviation** for each of these words.
The list will help you.

1 Avenue
2 January
3 Road
4 September
5 Street

6 August
7 Terrace
8 December
9 Square
10 October

Sept.	Terr.
Ave.	Dec.
Sq.	St.
Aug.	Oct.
Jan.	Rd

B Write the **abbreviations** for each of the following.

1 Royal Air Force

2 On Her Majesty's Service

3 Doctor

4 Police Constable

5 Post Office

6 Her Majesty's Ship

7 United Kingdom

8 Victoria Cross

9 British Broadcasting Corporation

Verbs (4)

Choose the correct **verb** to complete the sentences.

A   **was** or **were**

1 All the boys _____ playing football.
2 None of the animals _____ harmed by the fire.
3 They _____ making model planes.
4 Every girl _____ in the swimming pool.

B   **is** or **are**

1 Anybody _____ allowed to borrow a book.
2 Not one of the children _____ absent from school.
3 Every one of the bottles _____ broken.
4 All the children _____ visiting the museum.

C   **ate** or **eaten**

1 Susan had _____ all her sweets.
2 The greedy dog _____ his food very quickly.
3 Many cabbage leaves had been _____ by caterpillars.
4 Jane _____ an apple on her way to school.

D   **broke** or **broken**

1 A football _____ the classroom window.
2 This window has been _____ twice before.
3 Sue said that she had _____ the vase.
4 The vase _____ when Sue bumped into the table.

Vocabulary (2)

A Complete the following. The list of words will help you.

1 a _____ of pups
2 a _____ of sheep
3 a _____ of bees
4 a _____ of people
5 a _____ of cattle
6 a _____ of sailors
7 a _____ of teachers

8 a _____ of fish
9 a _____ of books
10 a _____ of trees
11 a _____ of flowers
12 a _____ of wolves
13 a _____ of soldiers
14 a _____ of ships

herd	crew	forest	litter	pack	fleet	swarm
bouquet	flock	regiment	library	crowd	staff	shoal

B Complete these sentences.

1 Bananas, mangoes and plums are all types of _____.
2 Freesias, lilies and carnations are all types of _____.
3 Salmon, tuna and herring are all types of _____.
4 Rubies, emeralds and sapphires are all types of _____.
5 Beetles, flies and grasshoppers are all types of _____.

C What would you expect to find

1 in a kettle ?
2 in an envelope ?
3 in a library ?
4 in a vase ?
5 in a gallery ?
6 in an aviary ?
7 in a greenhouse ?
8 in a hangar ?

9 in a safe ?
10 in a hutch ?
11 in a garage ?
12 in a sty ?
13 in a wardrobe ?
14 in a wallet ?
15 in a dustbin ?
16 in an aquarium ?

Joining sentences (2)

Choose the best word from the list to join each of the two short sentences.

A

| so   when   where   but   while |

1 I went to the shed. I found a frightened puppy.
2 Mary was sleeping. We were playing.
3 It was muddy. We put on our wellingtons.
4 She did her best. She did not win the prize.
5 John was climbing a tree. He saw the fire.

B

| but   before   so   because   which |

1 This is our secret cave. It is full of surprises.
2 David could not drink his tea. It was too hot.
3 Jenny looked for her kitten. She could not find it.
4 Sam began to shiver. He put on his coat.
5 Derek had a bath. He went to bed.

C

| but   though   while   who   yet |

1 We saw the policeman. He saved a lady from drowning.
2 The wind was very cold. It was the month of June.
3 Andrew was very clever. He was lazy.
4 Sue could not climb the rope. She tried her best.
5 Mark made a fire. Andrew put up the tent.

Vocabulary and spelling (3)

A The answers to these clues all have **ce** in them.

1 He helps to keep law and order.   __ __ __ __ c e __ __ __
2 A teacup stands on one.   __ __ __ c e __
3 A large lump of ice that floats in the sea.   __ c e __ __ __ __
4 Part of something.   __ __ __ c e
5 A house for a king or queen.   __ __ __ __ c e
6 Two times, or double.   __ __ __ c e
7 Doing something many times.   __ __ __ __ __ __ c e
8 A time when there is no war.   __ __ __ c e

B The answers to these clues all have **tch** in them.

1 A small clock, usually worn on your wrist.   __ __ t c h
2 The room where food is prepared and cooked.   __ __ t c h __ __
3 A home for a pet rabbit.   __ __ t c h
4 A bag sometimes carried by schoolchildren.   __ __ t c h __ __
5 A mark made with something sharp.   __ __ __ __ __ t c h
6 Looking at.   __ __ t c h __ __ __
7 To sew with thread.   __ __ __ t c h
8 Used by lame people to help them walk.   __ __ __ t c h __ __

C The answers to these clues all have **ck** in them.

1 A machine for telling the time.   __ __ __ c k
2 A covering for the foot and leg.   __ __ c k
3 To hit with the foot.   __ __ c k
4 A summer game.   __ __ __ c k __ __
5 A young farm bird.   __ __ __ c k __ __
6 A short coat.   __ __ c k __ __
7 Cups, saucers and plates.   __ __ __ c k __ __ __
8 Worn on a chain round the neck.   __ __ c k __ __ __ __

Comprehension (2)

It was a Sunday afternoon at the beginning of September. Ben was lying on the double bed which almost filled their small room. He was reading a comic, his hands cupped to his head, his legs in the air. Now and then he shifted his position, licked a finger to his lips, and turned the pages of the comic. Max was standing by the window gazing out into the back garden. He was watching his mother, who was by the low wire fence which divided the bungalows. She was talking to the people next door. They were called Johns. Mr. Johns was almost bald, his hair was white, and his face was brown, even in winter time. He didn't go to work; he never did anything except weed the garden and smoke his pipe.

From *The Haunted Mine* by Richard Potts
Reprinted by permission of Pan Books Ltd.

1 In which room was Ben and what was he doing?
2 Did Ben live in a house or a bungalow?
3 What was the name of the next door neighbours?
4 Who else do you think shared the double bed with Ben?
5 What was Ben's mother doing?
6 What divided the gardens of the two bungalows?
7 Write two things which show that Mr. Johns was old.
8 How did Mr. Johns spend most of his time?
9 Why do you think his face was always brown?
10 Was Ben lying on his front or back? Give a reason for your answer.

The apostrophe—to show ownership (1)

A Write out the following using the **apostrophe (')** to show there is **one owner**.

e.g. David's book

1 the babys toy	**9** the referees whistle
2 Peters bike	**10** the horses tail
3 the firemans helmet	**11** Carolyns car
4 the dogs kennel	**12** the giraffes neck
5 the birds feathers	**13** the cars tyres
6 the deers antlers	**14** the lions claws
7 the rabbits ears	**15** the gorillas cage
8 the teachers table	**16** the policemans radio

B Write these the short way.

e.g. the spade which belongs to Sam → Sam's spade

1 the pen belonging to Mark →
2 the pram belonging to Jill →
3 the tent which belongs to Adam →
4 the heat of the sun →
5 the garage of the car →
6 the coat belonging to mum →
7 the cage of the parrot →
8 the petals of the flower →
9 the caravan belonging to Mr. Brown →
10 the tail of the cat →

Vocabulary (3)

A In each of the following groups, write out the one word which includes all the others.

1	girls	men	people	boys	women
2	Moscow	Paris	London	Brussels	capitals
3	apple	fruit	date	orange	pear
4	cabbage	lettuce	turnip	vegetables	cauliflower
5	supper	breakfast	dinner	tea	meals
6	football	cricket	tennis	games	squash
7	table	furniture	chair	cupboard	bookcase
8	drum	recorder	piano	organ	instruments
9	vehicles	van	bus	taxi	lorry
10	Glasgow	Belfast	cities	Swansea	Leeds

B In each of the following groups, arrange the words in the order of size of the object, beginning with the smallest.

1	rat	pig	rabbit	horse	elephant
2	minute	week	second	day	hour
3	wren	starling	ostrich	seagull	turkey
4	city	village	house	country	continent
5	puddle	ocean	lake	sea	pond
6	cup	bath	kettle	eggcup	bucket
7	trunk	tree	twig	branch	leaf
8	shark	goldfish	cod	whale	shrimp
9	metre	millimetre	kilometre	centimetre	
10	yacht	liner	dinghy	rowing boat	supertanker

Verbs (5)

A Begin each of these sentences with **Yesterday**.

e.g. Anne **wins** the race.

Yesterday Anne **won** the race.

1 The dog **plays** in the garden.
2 The baker **bakes** a lot of bread.
3 The trawler **sails** to the White Sea.
4 Peter **arrives** at school at nine o'clock.
5 The farmer **chases** the dogs away from the sheep.
6 Paul **takes** a long time to do his maths.
7 Dad **drives** his car to the garage.
8 Tim **flies** his model aeroplane.
9 Sandra **feels** ill.
10 Our teacher **reads** a story to the class.

B Change the **verb** in bold type to show that something happens or is happening now.

1 The girl **spoke** with an American accent.
2 The boy **rubbed** his sore knee.
3 The thrush **hopped** about looking for worms.
4 Sarah always **found** time for reading.
5 Barry **brought** his young brother to school.
6 The dog **sat** outside the shop door.
7 The cars **stopped** at the traffic lights.
8 The workmen **dug** a deep hole.
9 The dog **begged** for a bone.
10 The bus **skidded** on the ice.

Vocabulary and spelling (4)

A The answers to these clues all have **pp** in them.

1	The last meal of the day.	— — p p — — —
2	A fruit.	— p p — —
3	Soft, comfortable shoes worn in the house.	— — — — p p — — — —
4	A reddish metal.	— — p p — —
5	A herring dried over smoke.	— — p p — —
6	A hot-tasting powdered spice.	— — p p — —
7	To come into sight.	— p p — — —
8	A small greyhound.	— — — p p — —

B The answers to these clues all have **gg** in them.

1	Cases and baggage used by a traveller.	— — g g — — —
2	Turning over the soil.	— — g g — — —
3	Someone who does throwing and balancing tricks.	— — g g — — —
4	A short, sharp knife.	— — g g — —
5	The largest.	— — g g — — —
6	To fight with something or someone.	— — — — g g — —
7	To laugh in a silly way.	— — g g — —
8	Rough and sharp at the edge.	— — g g — —

C The answers to these clues all have **dd** in them.

1	To walk in shallow water.	— — d d — —
2	When people get married.	— — d d — — —
3	The place where someone lives.	— d d — — — —
4	The centre.	— — d d — —
5	A seat on a horse or a bicycle.	— — d d — —
6	A small, poisonous snake.	— d d — —
7	Happening quickly.	— — d d — — — —
8	To interfere with something.	— — d d — —

Rhyming words

A Write out the word which **rhymes** with the word in bold type.

1	**pail**	fall	pill	sale	wall	fell
2	**pot**	goat	note	top	lit	knot
3	**die**	bee	high	say	may	lay
4	**done**	fun	sum	phone	wrong	gone
5	**pour**	our	low	for	fur	hour
6	**you**	bough	how	flew	bow	though
7	**frost**	post	lost	most	boast	toast
8	**bone**	none	sun	lone	won	bun
9	**care**	fear	here	fur	purr	hair
10	**knew**	bow	know	few	low	knot

B Write the missing word in each line. It must **rhyme** with the word in bold type.

1 **bawl** A wren is a very _____ bird.
2 **floor** Will you please _____ me a cup of tea?
3 **seat** I shall _____ you outside the Post Office.
4 **bean** Have you _____ my cat anywhere?
5 **flour** The rose is my favourite _____.
6 **white** I went to bed late last _____.
7 **fair** It is rude to _____ at anyone.
8 **might** I must _____ a letter to my pen friend.
9 **seek** Pam was _____ after her long illness.
10 **date** I had to _____ an hour for the bus.

The apostrophe—to show ownership (2)

A Write out the following using the **apostrophe (')** to show that there is **more than one owner**.

1 the ladies hats
2 the dogs dinners
3 the policemens boots
4 the soldiers guns
5 the sheeps tails
6 the footballers shirts
7 the childrens books
8 the insects wings

9 the firemens hoses
10 the foxes cubs
11 the mices tails
12 the sailors ship
13 the womens shoes
14 the boys changing room
15 the miners lamps
16 the workmens hut

B Write these the short way.
e.g. the trunks of the elephants
the elephants' trunks

1 the club for boys
2 the cage of the wolves
3 the cloakrooms for pupils
4 a library for children
5 a staffroom for teachers
6 the dressing rooms of the footballers
7 the fangs belonging to the snakes
8 the meeting of the workers
9 a hairdresser for ladies
10 the babies of the mothers

Improving sentences

A In place of each **adjective** in heavy type choose another from the list which will improve the sentence.

1 The **hungry** dog was trapped for six days in a cave.
2 The Jumbo jet has **big** engines.
3 **Large** waves crashed over the ship caught on the rocks.
4 The pyramids are **old** buildings in Egypt.
5 The climber was trapped on the **dangerous** cliffs.
6 It is very **moist** in the jungle.
7 The fox is said to be a **sly** animal.
8 The tramp's **odd** behaviour puzzled us.

ancient   cunning   humid   powerful   enormous   strange   starving   perilous

B The man dived into the water to rescue the boy.

By using **adjectives** this sentence can be made more interesting.

The **brave** man dived into the **deep** water to rescue the **terrified** boy.

Improve these sentences by adding suitable **adjectives**.

1 Last winter we had _____ snow, _____ frosts and _____ gales.
2 The _____ clowns wore _____ costumes at the circus.
3 Yesterday I saw a _____ man trying to cross a _____ road.
4 I enjoy a _____ _____ apple after my lunch.
5 The _____ motorist drove slowly in the _____ fog.
6 The _____ sheepdog rounded up the _____ sheep.
7 I saw the _____ firemen rescue two _____ ladies from the _____ house.
8 The _____ monkey climbed down the _____ tree and grabbed the _____ girl's ice cream.

Compound words

A Write the name of each picture. Show the two words which form the
compound word.

e.g. bull + dog → bulldog

B Now use each word in a sentence.

Mixed bag (2)

A Complete the following with a suitable **noun**.

1 Uncle is to nephew as aunt is to _____.
2 Foal is to horse as lamb is to _____.
3 Hat is to head as shoe is to _____.
4 Honey is to bee as milk is to _____.
5 Sound is to ear as taste is to _____.
6 Ear is to hear as eye is to _____.
7 Sing is to bird as grunt is to _____.
8 Table is to wood as window is to _____.

B Which **verb** in the brackets means the **opposite** of the word in heavy type?

1 **move**   (run   gallop   halt   race   walk)
2 **receive**   (have   buy   give   sell)
3 **arrive**   (come   depart   stay   enter)
4 **conceal**   (hide   reveal   bury   place)
5 **climb**   (ascend   scale   soar   rise   descend)
6 **repair**   (mend   break   make   alter)
7 **shut**   (fasten   lock   close   open)
8 **defend**   (protect   attack   help   support)

C Complete each sentence with an **adverb** made from the word in brackets.

1 The horse was galloping _____ towards the gate.   (quick)
2 The nurses _____ lifted the injured boy.   (careful)
3 The aeroplane landed _____ with a damaged engine.   (safe)
4 Terry wrote his story very _____.   (neat)
5 Grandad nodded his head _____.   (sleepy)
6 The tortoise moved _____ across the grass.   (slow)
7 The boys were working _____ on their canoe.   (busy)
8 The lions roared _____ at their trainer.   (angry)

Similar sounding words

Write out the sentences, completing them by choosing the correct word from the brackets.

1 My football cost £3 in the _____ at the sports shop.   (sale, sail)

2 You must _____ your brother outside school.   (meet, meat)

3 The bus _____ to town is now 12p.   (fair, fare)

4 Sally was in _____ when she broke her arm.   (pain, pane)

5 Mark looked _____ when he was ill in bed.   (pale, pail)

6 Our house is on a busy _____ road.   (mane, main)

7 A _____ tree hasn't any leaves.   (bear, bare)

8 The football team lost _____ first match today.   (their, there)

9 Please bring your book _____ .   (hear, here)

10 The car was too _____ so dad didn't buy it.   (dear, deer)

11 We went on the dodgems at the _____.   (fare, fair)

12 A lion has a long _____ .   (main, mane)

13 The _____ on the yacht was torn by the strong wind.   (sale, sail)

14 The _____ is a timid animal.   (dear, deer)

15 A _____ is a kind of bucket.   (pale, pail)

16 John kicked the ball which broke a _____ of glass.   (pain, pane)

17 I don't think the _____ is cooked enough.   (meat, meet)

18 The polar _____ eats a lot of fish.   (bare, bear)

19 Put the bicycle _____ .   (there, their)

20 Don't shout! I can _____ you.   (hear, here)

Comprehension (3)

Cornerstones stood empty and deserted. The house had been like this for months. Even the 'For Sale' notice was looking old and neglected, slumped against the front gate-post where it had been blown by the wind. Behind the house, the large, rambling garden, from which you could look down into the town in one direction and across the hills in the other, was overgrown with weeds and grasses. In the orchard, last autumn's apples lay yellow and shrivelled beneath the bare trees in beds of damp leaves. *Cornerstones* itself had paint peeling from the front door, and the windows were shrouded with brown dirt.

From *Nobody's House* by Martin Hall
Copyright © Derrick Sherwin & Martin Hall 1976
published by Fontana/Collins

1 What was *Cornerstones*?
2 Which two words show that no one lived at *Cornerstones*?
3 Did the house have a big or a small back garden?
4 What is an orchard?
5 Write down the two **adjectives** which describe the apples.
6 What was written on the notice board?
7 Was the house in a country district or in a town?
8 Write out the sentence which shows that the house needed repainting.
9 Was this description written in summer or winter? Give a reason for your answer.
10 Use a dictionary to find the meaning of:
  deserted, neglected, slumped, shrivelled, shrouded.

Answers

Page 2 Verbs (1)
A 1 – 10 Check your child's words.
B 1 – 10 Check your child's words.

Page 3 Nouns
A 1 horse **2** chocolate **3** water **4** apple **5** dinner **6** policeman, thief **7** cat, roof
8 boys, girls, cinema **9** Leaves, tree **10** books, library
B 1 – 10 Check your child's answers.
C Check your child's answers.

Page 4 Picture comprehension (1)
Check your child's words are appropriate.

Page 5 Punctuation
A Check your child's use of capital letters and full stops.
B 1 The Jumbo jet landed safely.
2 Have you seen our new caretaker?
3 A tortoise has a hard shell.
4 We enjoyed Tim's party.
5 Will you play football with me?
6 Did you see that unusual bird?
7 Our lawn needs cutting.
8 Why don't you eat your dinner?
C 1 The butcher sells lamb, beef, pork and sausages.
2 The cricket season is May, June, July, August and September.
3 The sailor had been to China, Japan, India and Australia.
4 I saw snowdrops, crocuses, daffodils and tulips in the park.
5 Oak, ash, beech, sycamore and elm are deciduous trees.
6 My favourite football teams are Everton, Arsenal, Motherwell, Newcastle and Linfield.

Page 6 Adverbs
A 1 Snow fell **heavily** on the mountain.
2 The girls ran **quickly** down the hill.
3 Anne slept **soundly** after her long swim.
4 Our team won the swimming gala **easily** this year.
5 The sun shone **brightly** all morning.
6 The old man walked **slowly** up the stairs.
7 Bill bought his bicycle **cheaply** at the sale.
8 The hungry dog ate his food **greedily**.
B 1 – 8 Check that your child's adverbs are appropriate for the sentences.

Page 7 Vocabulary and spelling (1)
A 1 key **2** honey **3** donkey **4** money **5** chimney **6** monkey
B 1 saw **2** paw **3** straw **4** law **5** jaw **6** draw
C 1 bicycle **2** apple **3** eagle **4** rifle **5** candle **6** whistle

Page 8 Adjectives (1)
A 1 pink **2** blue **3** big **4** electric **5** long **6** tall, old **7** tall, old **8** wet, grumpy
9 long, thin, fat **10** huge, rough
B 1 juicy orange **2** hot dinner **3** fast car **4** heavy load **5** red flower **6** loud noise
7 woollen sweater **8** deep lake **9** funny clown **10** steep hill

Page 9 Pictures and sentences
1 – 8 Check that your child's sentences describe the pictures.

Page 10 Alphabetical order (1)
A 1 bark, bench, big, bold, bull
2 above, acorn, air, animal, arrow
3 camel, chess, clock, crow, cut
4 paint, pencil, place, pram, puzzle
5 sail, seal, seven, shed, skin
6 dart, desk, dig, door, duck
7 make, meat, milk, money, music
8 talk, tent, thief, tie, tomato
9 wasp, week, wheat, wife, wrist
10 rain, real, rhyme, ribbon, rust
B 1 lunch **2** nine **3** floor **4** edge **5** glue **6** hymn **7** jungle **8** valley **9** past
10 dwarf

Page 11 Joining sentences (1)
A 1 Here is the girl **who** is a good swimmer.
2 I caught the dog **who** bit the boy.
3 The teacher praised Tom **who** had written an exciting story.
4 I thanked the policeman **who** found my bike.
5 We travelled on the train **which** went to Cardiff.
6 Jim caught a fish **which** was swimming in the pond.
7 This is my aunty **who** lives in Belfast.
8 Mrs Rigby has two sons **who** are very tall.
B 1 Tim slipped and fell **but** he did not hurt himself.
2 She had measles **so** she could not go to school.
3 Brenda returned the shoes to the shop **because** they were too small.
4 The hotel was burned down **but** no lives were lost.
5 She could not speak **because** she had a sore throat.
6 The garage was closed **so** we could not buy any petrol.
7 We went to the forest **because** we wanted to see a woodpecker.
8 The policeman chased the dog **but** he did not catch it.

Page 12 Gender
A 1 princess **2** woman **3** girl **4** aunt **5** daughter **6** bride **7** mother **8** witch
9 grandmother **10** goddess
B 1 actor **2** mayor **3** king **4** nephew **5** brother **6** waiter **7** widower **8** he **9** hero
10 husband
C 1 lion **2** goose **3** buck **4** mare **5** tiger **6** bull **7** vixen **8** ram **9** hen **10** stag

Page 13 Verbs (2)
A 1 kicked **2** ran **3** jumped **4** skidded **5** crawled **6** ate, played **7** cut, fed
8 waved, cheered **9** cut, fell **10** purrs, stroke
B Check your child's answers.

Page 14 Adjectives (2)
A 1 bright **2** clumsy **3** difficult **4** playful **5** dark **6** icy **7** windy **8** idle
B 1 a long day **2** a happy girl **3** a fast train **4** a wet towel **5** an old horse
6 a fresh loaf **7** a strong lion **8** a sweet apple **9** a deep pond **10** a wild animal
11 a right/correct answer **12** a rude girl

Page 15 Plurals
A 1 dogs **2** boxes **3** brushes **4** girls **5** hands **6** glasses **7** matches **8** lakes **9** foxes **10** flowers
B 1 holidays **2** cities **3** armies **4** boys **5** keys **6** stories **7** monkeys **8** ponies **9** ladies **10** valleys
C 1 halves **2** cargoes **3** loaves **4** thieves **5** potatoes **6** wolves **7** volcanoes **8** leaves **9** elves **10** tomatoes
D 1 days **2** scarves **3** chiefs **4** lilies **5** children **6** churches **7** pianos **8** women **9** feet **10** papers

Page 16 Pronouns
A 1 I **2** He **3** She **4** me **5** They **6** You **7** We, you **8** It
B 1 She **2** It **3** They **4** It **5** them **6** He **7** her **8** him

Page 17 Adjectives (3)
A cruel, fierce, friendly, cheap, silent
B 1 huge **2** leafy **3** blazing **4** comfortable **5** fast **6** wet **7** busy **8** howling **9** juicy **10** exciting
C 1 Check your child's adjectives.

Page 18 Picture comprehension (2)
Check your child's sentences explain what is happening in the pictures.

Page 19 Vocabulary and spelling (2)
A 1 bottom **2** rotten **3** attic **4** butter **5** cottage **6** pretty
B 1 mirror **2** narrow **3** tomorrow **4** hurry **5** strawberry **6** arrow
C 1 ballet **2** swallow **3** yellow **4** tall **5** collar **6** village

Page 20 Contractions
A 1 he's **2** she's **3** it's **4** who's **5** that's **6** where's **7** what's **8** there's
B 1 we'll **2** he'll **3** you'll **4** she'll **5** I'll **6** they'll
C 1 we're **2** I'm **3** they're **4** we've **5** they've **6** I've
D 1 does not **2** were not **3** have not **4** we will **5** they are **6** I am **7** that is **8** they will **9** when is **10** cannot

Page 21 Groups
A 1 mammals **2** colours **3** tools **4** fruit **5** vehicles **6** months **7** trees **8** fish **9** flowers **10** birds
B 1 tulip **2** Asia **3** carrot **4** grass **5** ship **6** carpet **7** hen **8** face

Page 22 Verbs (3)
1 thrown **2** limped **3** leaped **4** dashed **5** ripped **6** thundered **7** marched **8** roared **9** kicked **10** gushed **11** dived **12** snatched

Page 23 Picture comprehension (3)
Check that your child's sentences explain what is happening in the pictures.

Page 24 Vocabulary (1)
A 1 shepherd **2** mechanic **3** coastguard **4** chemist **5** sculptor **6** nurse **7** optician **8** joiner **9** steeplejack **10** caretaker
B 1 waitress **2** artist **3** bakery **4** dentist **5** brewery **6** explorer **7** plumber **8** orchard **9** jockey **10** desert

Page 25 Questions

A 1 Where did you put your hamster's food?
2 How is you mother feeling after her operation?
3 Did you enjoy your trip to the zoo?
4 Will you lend me your bike please?
5 Which of these puppies would you like?
6 Why were you not at school this morning?
7 Whose football boots are these?
8 What would you like to do tomorrow?
9 Have you seen the exhibition of models?
10 Who said that our team won?
B 1 - 10 Check that your child's questions are appropriate for the answers given.

Page 26 Similar meanings

A 1 hard **2** money **3** crying **4** mend **5** rich **6** help **7** right **8** starts **9** little **10** join
B 1 reply **2** brave **3** shining **4** drop **5** show **6** gather **7** brief **8** conceal **9** draw
10 summit

Page 27 Adjectives (4)

1 – 12 Check that your child's adjectives are suitable.

Page 28 Alphabetical order (2)

1 magic, male, marble, mast, mayor
2 page, pale, parcel, path, paw
3 table, tadpole, tale, tap, taxi
4 wagon, walrus, war, watch, wax
5 beach, bee, bell, bend, berry
6 cabbage, cactus, cage, camel, card
7 daffodil, dagger, dark, date, dawn
8 face, fair, fall, farm, father
9 grab, grease, grip, grow, grunt
10 veal, vehicle, velvet, verb, vestry
B 1 bill **2** cider **3** deep **4** weigh **5** rice **6** magic **7** hand **8** fed **9** naval **10** shed

Page 29 Mixed bag (1)

A 1 his **2** theirs **3** yours **4** ours **5** mine **6** hers **7** mine **8** hers **9** theirs **10** yours
B 1 snow **2** nails **3** coal **4** bee **5** rake **6** ice **7** grass **8** lead **9** feather **10** honey

Page 30 Opposites

A 1 glad **2** take **3** end **4** bad **5** small **6** quiet **7** dirty **8** cold **9** night **10** deep
B 1 O **2** S **3** O **4** O **5** S **6** O **7** O **8** S **9** O **10** S **11** O **12** O **13** S **14** S **15** O **16** S

Page 31 Comprehension (1)

1 Littlenose lived a long time ago because he lived during the Ice Age.
2 Four foods that Littlenose ate which we eat today are meat, fish, fruit and vegetables.
3 Littlenose ate caterpillars which wouldn't be nice to eat.
4 Three things that Littlenose didn't eat but which we eat are sugar, jam and sticky buns.
5 Two wild animals which we can still see today are rhinoceros and elk.
6 An animal that is extinct is the sabre-toothed tiger.
7 Honey was used instead of sugar.

8 Littlenose got his honey from the nests of wild bees.

9 Collecting honey was dangerous because the bees were ferocious.

10 Bees defend themselves by stinging people.

Page 32 Abbreviations

A 1 Ave. **2** Jan. **3** Rd **4** Sept. **5** St. **6** Aug. **7** Terr. **8** Dec. **9** Sq. **10** Oct.

B 1 RAF **2** OHMS **3** Dr **4** PC **5** PO **6** HMS **7** UK **8** VC **9** BBC

Page 33 Verbs (4)

A 1 were **2** was **3** were **4** was

B 1 is **2** is **3** is **4** are

C 1 eaten **2** ate **3** eaten **4** ate

D 1 broke **2** broken **3** broken **4** broke

Page 34 Vocabulary (2)

1 litter **2** flock **3** swarm **4** crowd **5** herd **6** crew **7** staff **8** shoal **9** library
10 forest **11** bouquet **12** pack **13** regiment **14** fleet

B 1 fruit **2** flowers **3** fish **4** jewels/gems **5** insects

C 1 water **2** letter **3** books **4** flowers **5** paintings **6** birds **7** plants **8** aeroplanes
9 money **10** a rabbit **11** a car **12** a pig **13** clothes **14** money **15** rubbish **16** fish

Page 35 Joining sentences (2)

A 1 I went to the shed **where** I found a frightened puppy.

2 Mary was sleeping **while** we were playing.

3 It was muddy **so** we put on our Wellingtons.

4 She did her best **but** she did not win the prize.

5 John was climbing a tree **when** he saw the fire.

B 1 This is our secret cave **which** is full of surprises.

2 David could not drink his tea **because** it was too hot.

3 Jenny looked for her kitten **but** she could not find it.

4 Sam began to shiver **so** he put on his coat.

5 Derek had a bath **before** he went to bed.

C 1 We saw the policeman **who** saved a lady from drowning.

2 The wind was very cold **yet** it was the month of June.

3 Andrew was very clever **but** he was lazy.

4 Sue could not climb the rope **though** she tried her best.

5 Mark made a fire **while** Andrew put up the tent.

Page 36 Vocabulary and spelling (3)

A 1 policeman **2** saucer **3** iceberg **4** piece **5** palace **6** twice **7** practice **8** peace

B 1 watch **2** kitchen **3** hutch **4** satchel **5** scratch **6** watching **7** stitch **8** crutches

C 1 clock **2** sock **3** kick **4** cricket **5** chicken **6** jacket **7** crockery **8** necklace

Page 37 Comprehension (2)

1 Ben was in the bedroom reading a comic.

2 Ben lived in a bungalow.

3 The neighbours' name was the Johns.

4 Ben shared the double bed with Max.

5 Ben's mother was talking to the people next door.

6 The two gardens were divided by a low wire fence.

7 Two things which show that Mr. John was old are
his almost bald head and white hair.

8 Mr. Johns spent most of his time weeding the garden.

9 Mr. John's face was always brown because he was always outside in the garden.

10 Ben was lying on his front because he was resting on his hands and had to shift his position to turn the pages of his comic.

Page 38 The apostrophe – to show ownership (1)

A 1 the baby's toy **2** Peter's bike **3** the fireman's helmet **4** the dog's kennel
5 the bird's feathers **6** the deer's antlers **7** the rabbit's ears **8** the teacher's table
9 the referee's whistle **10** the horse's tail **11** Carolyn's car **12** the giraffe's neck
13 the car's tyres **14** the lion's claws **15** the gorilla's cage **16** the policeman's radio
B 1 Mark's pen **2** Jill's pram **3** Adam's tent **4** the sun's heat **5** the car's garage
6 mum's coat **7** the parrot's cage **8** the flower's petals **9** Mr Brown's caravan
10 the cat's tail

Page 39 Vocabulary (3)

A 1 people **2** capitals **3** fruit **4** vegetables **5** meals **6** games **7** furniture
8 instruments **9** vehicles **10** cities
B 1 rat, rabbit, pig, horse, elephant
2 second, minute, hour, day, week
3 wren, starling, seagull, turkey, ostrich
4 house, village, city, country, continent
5 puddle, pond, lake, sea, ocean
6 eggcup, cup, kettle, bucket, bath
7 leaf, twig, branch, trunk, tree
8 shrimp, goldfish, cod, shark, whale
9 millimetre, centimetre, metre, kilometre
10 dinghy, rowing boat, yacht, liner, supertanker

Page 40 Verbs (5)

A 1 Yesterday the dog **played** in the garden.
2 Yesterday the baker **baked** a lot of bread.
3 Yesterday the trawler **sailed** to the White Sea.
4 Yesterday Peter **arrived** at school at nine o'clock.
5 Yesterday the farmer **chased** the dogs away from the sheep.
6 Yesterday Paul **took** a long time to do his maths.
7 Yesterday Dad **drove** his car to the garage.
8 Yesterday Tim **flew** his model aeroplane.
9 Yesterday Sandra **felt** ill.
10 Yesterday our teacher **read** a story to the class.
B 1 The girl **speaks/is speaking** with an American accent.
2 The boy **rubs/is rubbing** his sore knee.
3 The thrush **hops/is hopping** about looking for worms.
4 Sarah always **finds** time for reading.
5 Barry **brings/is bringing** his young brother to school.
6 The dog **sits/is sitting** outside the shop door.
7 The cars **stop/are stopping** at the traffic lights.
8 The workmen **dig/are digging** a deep hole.
9 The dog **begs/is begging** for a bone.
10 The bus **skids/is skidding** on the ice.

Page 41 Vocabulary and spelling (4)
A **1** supper **2** apple **3** slippers **4** copper **5** kipper **6** pepper **7** appear **8** whippet
B **1** luggage **2** digging **3** juggler **4** dagger **5** biggest **6** struggle **7** giggle
8 jagged
C **1** paddle **2** wedding **3** address **4** middle **5** saddle **6** adder **7** suddenly
8 meddle

Page 42 Rhyming words
A **1** sale **2** knot **3** high **4** fun **5** for **6** flew **7** lost **8** lone **9** hair **10** few
B **1** tall **2** pour **3** meet **4** seen **5** flower **6** night **7** stare **8** write **9** weak **10** wait

Page 43 The apostrophe – to show ownership (2)
A **1** the ladies' hats
2 the dogs' dinners
3 the policemen's boots
4 the soldiers' guns
5 the sheep's tails
6 the footballers' shirts
7 the children's books
8 the insects' wings
9 the firemen's hoses
10 the foxes' cubs
11 the mice's tails
12 the sailors' ship
13 the women's shoes
14 the boys' changing room
15 the miners' lamps
16 the workmen's hut
B **1** the boys' club
2 the wolves' cage
3 the pupils' cloakroom
4 the children's library
5 the teachers' staffroom
6 the footballers' dressingrooms
7 the snake's fangs
8 the workers' meeting
9 the ladies' hairdresser
10 the mothers' babies

Page 44 Improving sentences
A **1** The **starving** dog was trapped for six days in a cave.
2 The Jumbo has **powerful** engines.
3 **Enormous** waves crashed over the ship caught on the rocks.
4 The pyramids are **ancient** buildings in Egypt.
5 The climber was trapped on the **perilous** cliffs.
6 It is very **humid** in the jungle.
7 The fox is said to be a **cunning** animal.
8 The tramp's **strange** behaviour puzzled us.
B Check your child has used suitable adjectives to complete the sentences.

Page 45 Compound words

A 2 wheel + barrow = wheelbarrow
3 water + fall = waterfall
4 butter + fly = butterfly
5 wind + mill = windmill
6 trap + door = trapdoor
7 port + hole = porthole
8 arm + chair = armchair
9 tooth + brush = toothbrush
10 black + board = blackboard
11 light + house = lighthouse
12 cup + board = cupboard
B Check your child's sentences.

Page 46 Mixed bag (2)

A 1 niece **2** sheep **3** foot **4** cow **5** tongue **6** see **7** pig **8** glass
B 1 halt **2** give **3** depart **4** reveal **5** descend **6** break **7** open **8** attack
C 1 quickly **2** carefully **3** safely **4** neatly **5** sleepily **6** slowly **7** busily **8** angrily

Page 47 Similar sounding words

1 sale **2** meet **3** fare **4** pain **5** pale **6** main **7** bare **8** their **9** here **10** dear **11** fair **12** mane **13** sail **14** deer **15** pail **16** pane **17** meat **18** bear **19** there **20** hear

Page 48 Comprehension (3)

1 *Cornerstones* was a house.
2 Two words that show that no one lived at *Cornerstones* are 'empty' and 'deserted'.
3 It had a big back garden.
4 An orchard is where fruit trees grow.
5 Two adjectives that describe the apples are 'yellow' and 'shrivelled'.
6 'For Sale' was written on the notice board.
7 The house was in a country district.
8 The sentence which shows that the house needed repainting is: '*Cornerstones* itself had paint peeling from the front door...'
9 The description was written in winter because it states: 'last autumn's apples...'.
10 deserted – empty
neglected – not been cared for
slumped – fallen heavily or suddenly
shrivelled – to be shrunken and withered
shrouded – covered